Edition Schott

Paul Hindemith
1895 – 1963

Meditation

aus dem Tanzspiel „Nobilissima Visione"

für Viola und Klavier
for Viola and Piano

ED 3684
ISMN 979-0-001-04402-8

www.schott-music.com

Mainz · London · Berlin · Madrid · New York · Paris · Prague · Tokyo · Toronto
© 1938 SCHOTT MUSIC GmbH & Co. KG, Mainz · © renewed 1966 · Printed in Germany

Meditation

Paul Hindemith
1895–1963

Sehr langsam (♩ etwa 46)

Viola

Meditation

Paul Hindemith
1895—1963